the Brownie

Annual 1985

edited by Penny Morris

This annual belongs to . . .

Jayne MacDonald

£2.99

Lifeboat Ahoy!

by Penny Morris

Founded in 1824 by William Hillary, the Royal National Lifeboat Institution is the oldest national lifeboat service in the world. The main aim of the Institution is the saving of life at sea, and since it started over 109,000 people have been saved. To find out more about this admirable service I took some Brownies to R.N.L.I. headquarters at Poole, in Dorset, and then to the lifeboat station at Swanage.

On the ground floor of R.N.L.I. headquarters is a museum, displaying models, paintings and equipment connected with the history of the lifeboat service. Prior to 1824 there had been several local lifeboat societies around the coast but no national organisation. Now there are over 200 lifeboat stations around the coast of the United Kingdom and the Republic of Ireland, providing a permanent search and rescue service up to 30 miles out to sea. The R.N.L.I. depends entirely on donations and voluntary contributions for funds, and saves over 1,000 lives every year.

Pack Leaders Ellie Watts and Dina Pothin were fascinated by the detail on some of the models in the museum. ▼

The early lifeboatmen wore bright yellow oilskins.

I would like to thank the staff of the R.N.L.I. headquarters at Poole, and the Coxswain and crew of the Swanage lifeboat for their help in preparing this feature.

photographs by Tony Rose

On the 2nd floor is the technical department where draughtsmen, engineers and surveyors design, test and adapt lifeboats and equipment, always seeking to improve the efficiency and safety of the boats. Designing the boats is a skilled job, as they must be small enough to get close beside wrecks and ships in distress to rescue the passengers and crew, but strong enough to withstand the worst weather conditions. They must be well equipped with navigation, communication and survival gear, and stable enough to make capsizing unlikely. All modern lifeboats are designed to be self-righting, so if they do capsize they automatically turn the right way up.

Up on the 4th floor is the Central Operations and Information Room (C.O.I.R.) which is manned 24 hours a day and keeps a check on any lifeboats in difficult or complex conditions. When there is a casualty at sea, it is usually the coastguard service that first hears of it, and decides whether to call on the lifeboat service for assistance. The coastguard co-ordinates all search and rescue work at sea, and they keep the C.O.I.R. informed about the situation. The C.O.I.R. also organises the movement of new and relief boats, and keeps records of all rescues. On the wall is a huge chart listing all the lifeboat stations around the coast, and showing the type of boat and method of launching.

Outside stands a statue of a nineteenth century lifeboatman looking out to sea. It is a copy of a memorial statue erected in Margate in memory of nine lifeboatmen drowned in 1897.

Across the road is the depot, where new boats are developed and tested and current boats are serviced. Relief boats are also kept here, ready to replace any damaged boats at short notice. Due to the careful maintenance of the lifeboats, most have an operational life of 25-30 years.

Since 1963 the R.N.L.I. has used inflatable lifeboats for inshore rescues. These are not suitable for use in bad weather, and are most frequently used to rescue swimmers in distress and people in small pleasure boats who are in difficulties.

Inside the depot everything to equip the lifeboats is stored, ready to be despatched within one hour of receiving a request for equipment from a lifeboat station. Nylon rope is used on the lifeboats as it is very strong. ▼

This 'bow pudding' (a rope fender) will take a week to make and should last ten years. As well as traditional items like anchors, compasses and even brandy, the depot also supplies electronic aids, such as radios, echo sounders, and radar. ▼

Special lifejackets are made here too, incorporating a whistle, a safety line, and a light which is activated on contact with salt water and is visible from half a mile away. They also have built-in buoyancy which automatically brings the wearer to the surface of the water face-upwards.

The Swanage lifeboat station, which houses a 36'6" Rother lifeboat, was first established in 1875. ▼

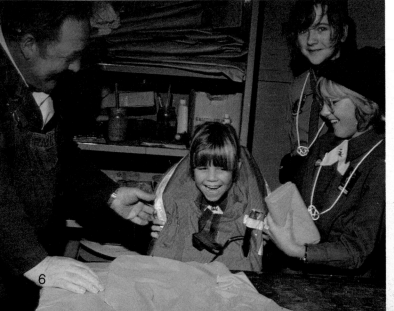

Inside hangs waterproof clothing ready for the crew to jump into when the boat is called out. Each crew member has a pair of fluorescent orange bib-and-brace trousers, a jacket, boots, a safety helmet, and a lifejacket.

This machinery is used to winch the boat back up the slipway into the boathouse, so it is ready in position next time it is needed. Each lifeboat station employs a full-time mechanic to look after the boat and ensure it is in working condition all the time.

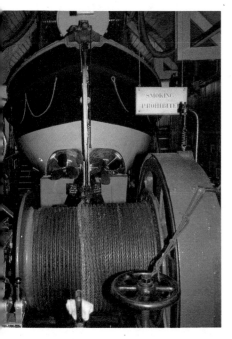

Lifeboats are launched in one of three ways: down a slipway, as here at Swanage; from a carriage pushed out across the beach by a tractor, as for example at Bridlington; or from a permanent mooring in a harbour or estuary, as at Poole.

Coxswain Vick Marsh is also the mechanic of the Swanage lifeboat, and has been in the lifeboat service for over 20 years.

Anyone who is physically fit can volunteer to serve on a lifeboat, and nowadays women are accepted to crew on inflatable lifeboats. When the boat is called out the crew are alerted either by phone, personal bleeper, or the firing of maroon rockets. ▼

When the boat returns from a mission the crew have the difficult task of reversing up to the slipway, and positioning the six-inch wide keel in the nine-inch groove on the slipway, ready for the boat to be winched up. ▼

Once the boat is in position lines are attached and the winch turned on. ▶

Nifty Knitting

You could make these clothes for a Sindy doll, using wool left over from a larger garment (use double-knitting or 4 ply).

Poncho

Using no 8 (4mm) needles cast on 1 stitch.
Knit 1, then increase 1 stitch, and continue to knit rows, increasing 1 stitch at the beginning of each row until you have 28 stitches on the needle.
Next row: knit 8 stitches, cast off 12, knit 8 stitches.
Next row: knit 8 stitches, cast on 12, knit 8 stitches.
Knit 2 together at the beginning of every row until last stitch.
Cast off.

Scarf

Using no 8 (4mm) needles, cast on 7 stitches.
Knit each row until the scarf is the required length, then cast off. If you have more than one colour of wool, you could make the scarf stripy.

Hat

Using no 8 (4mm) needles cast on 26 stitches.
Knit 4 rows in garter stitch (all knit).
Then change to stocking stitch (1 row knit, 1 row purl) and work until the knitting measures 1¼ inches (3cm).
Knit 2 together at the beginning of the next 4 rows.
Fasten off by threading wool through each stitch, pull firmly to gather them up, and stitch securely.
Sew up the side seam, and add a bobble if you like.

Dress

Using no 12 (2¾mm) needles, cast on 59 stitches.
Next row: knit 1, *purl 1, knit 1, repeat from * to end of row.
Knit another row the same as this.
Then knit 8 rows in stocking stitch (1 row knit, 1 row purl).
Next row: knit 2, knit 2 together, * knit 4, knit 2 together, repeat from *, to last stitch, knit 1.
You should now have 49 stitches on your needle.

Continue to knit in stocking stitch until the work measures 2 inches (5cm), ending with a purl row.
Next row: knit 1, knit 2 together, * knit 3, knit 2 together, repeat from *, to last stitch, knit 1.
You should now have 39 stitches on your needles.
Continue in stocking stitch until the work measures 3 inches (8cm), ending with a purl row.
Next row: knit 2 together, *knit 2, knit 2 together, repeat from * to last stitch, knit 1.
You should now have 29 stitches on your needle.
Next row: purl 13, purl 2 together, purl 14 (28 stitches).
Work 10 rows in knit 1, purl 1 rib.
Next row: cast off in rib 7 stitches, knit to last 7 stitches, cast off in rib these 7 stitches.
With wrong sides facing, rejoin the yarn to the 14 stitches on your needle.
* Purl 7, then turn and work 2 rows in stocking stitch on these 7 stitches.
Next row: knit 3, knit 2 together, knit 2.
Next row: purl 6.
Next row: knit 2, knit 2 together, knit 2.
Next row: purl 5.
Next row: knit 2, knit 2 together, knit 1.
Next row: purl 4.
Next row: knit 1, knit 2 together, knit 1.
Next row: purl 3
Next row: knit 1, knit 2 together.
Next row: purl 2 together, then slip the 1 remaining stitch onto a crochet hook and work 22 chain to make a tie for the halter of the dress. *
With wrong sides facing, rejoin yarn to the 7 stitches left, and work from * to * to complete.
Join the back seam of the dress.

Jean Hopkins

9

Did you know there are numerous wild 'cats' and 'dogs' in the fields, woods, hedgebanks and gardens near your home? No, I do not mean the four-legged, hairy, barking or miaowing animals, although there are probably many of those too. I am referring to flowers, grasses and shrubs that have 'cat' or 'dog' in their name.

The best known is probably the pink or whitish Dog Rose of summer, with bottle-shaped red hips, that forms bushes or scrambles over hedgerows, adorned with numerous flowers. It has been called the Dog Rose since the Romans lived in Britain over 1,500 years ago because it was then believed a medicine made from it cured a dog bite.

But the name of the pretty pale blue or purple Dog Violet, flowering on hedgebanks and heaths from May to August, with heart-shaped or nearly round leaves, has a different meaning. In this case 'Dog' was originally used as a word of disgrace or contempt because the flower has no scent, unlike the similar but smaller blue or white Sweet Violet.

The Dog (or Ox-Eye) Daisy, with its large white and yellow flowers as much as two inches across, flowers from June to August in meadows and waste places, often in neglected churchyards. Many years ago children used to thread the flowerheads on a thin cord or strong cotton to tie around the brims of their hats as a decoration. In Scotland it is called the Horse Gowan, but 'Dog' was used in one of its English names to mean larger than the very common Field Daisy.

Dog's Mercury commonly carpets large areas of shade in woods and thickets and the bottom of tall hedges in springtime. The spikes of greenish-yellow flowers are not particularly attractive. The Mercury part of the name was given because it was thought the Roman god Mercury discovered it could be used as a medicine, probably for treating dogs, as it is poisonous to human beings.

The shapes of flowering heads of grass have also been given names that describe them. Dog's-tail Grass, very common in dry pastures, meadows and on waste ground, has a three-inch-long spike of flowers in June and July. Wheat Grass, very common in hedges and shady places, flowering in June and July, is also known as Dog's Wheat because dogs eat its leaves as a medicine. Cat's-tail Grass has a long green spike tinted with pink or white, flowering in meadows and pastures from June to September.

The only shrub with a 'doggy' name is the Dogwood, found in hedges and sides of woodlands. The pointed, egg-shaped leaves grow in opposite pairs and have wavy edges. Its creamy-white, star-shaped flowers grow in clusters, becoming small dark purple berries in autumn. Other names for it are Dogberry and Dogcherry, but it has no association with proper dogs. Properly it should be called Dagwood,

illustrated by David Webb

CATS and DOGS

because its wood was formerly used to make what country people called dags – skewers for meat.

Cat's Eye is the country name for Germander Speedwell. It has cheerful, bright blue flowers, about half an inch across, in May and June, which look like cat's eyes. Sometimes when the plants are growing together in large numbers the flowers form a mass of blue on sloping banks and hedgebottoms. It is a garden weed and is also known in some areas as Bird's-Eye.

Cat's-foot is another country name for Ground Ivy, not really an Ivy, but related to Catmint. It trails along the ground at hedgebottoms and near woods, its stems bearing heads of bright purple-blue flowers from April to June. The purple-green leaves are rounded, kidney-shaped, rather like the shape of a cat's front feet, hence its rural name.

Cat's Valerian or Great Valerian is a plant of the stream and riverside, wet meadows and swampy woodlands, often growing in abundance. The tall stems bear crowded heads of pink, flesh-coloured or white flowers from June to August. The notched leaves are in opposite pairs and form two rows of narrow leaflets the same pattern as those of the Ash tree. It is also called All-Heal as its roots were used by herbalists to make medicines for various illnesses. When the plants are cut down and the stems and leaves allowed to dry they make a scent that is attractive to cats, which roll about on it as they do on Catmint.

Catmint has soft, hairy, whitish, heart-shaped leaves and stems. It grows on banks and waste ground. The wild Catmint, which is not very common, has small white flowers dotted with crimson in July and August. The garden Catmint is often grown by gardeners and has spikes of blue or mauve flowers. It has a strong aromatic smell which is especially attractive to cats, who love to rub their coat against it or roll about on the plant, hence its name.

Cat's-Ear looks rather like, and is related to, the Dandelion, but the stem is branched, each branch having a yellow flower from June to September. It grows in meadows, dry fields and on waysides. The leaves are all at ground level and resemble Dandelion leaves. It gets its name from the small bracts or tiny leaves near the branches on the flower stem, which look like cat's ears.

Of course it must not be forgotten that some types of tree – Hazel, Willow, Poplar – bear catkins as flower·spikes, so called because of their similarity to a cat's tail:

Lastly, the word caterpillar for the larvae of a moth or butterfly is very old. The pillar part came from the Latin *pilus* which means hair. Long ago it was thought by people the caterpillar was a sort of 'worm' with legs, covered with hairs like a hairy cat, so the name has survived. Really it should be called a pillarcat!

by Alan Major

11

make a spice rope

by Rosemary Dines

Spice ropes used to be hung in the kitchen as decoration and to get rid of cooking smells. You could fill yours with lavender and hang it in a wardrobe or cupboard if you prefer. To make one you will need:

- ☐ One brass or wooden ring approximately 3 cm (1¼″) across
- ☐ Twelve pieces of wool 1.5 m (5′) long
- ☐ Three circles of material 15 cm (6″) in diameter, pinked round the edges if you have pinking shears
- ☐ Scraps of coloured wool
- ☐ Herbs, spices or lavender

What to do:

1. Fold the twelve pieces of wool in half and fix to the ring like this:

2. Divide into three sections with eight strands of wool in each section.
3. Plait, leaving about 15 cm (6″) unplaited at the bottom, and tie with a piece of coloured wool.
4. Put a heaped teaspoonful of herbs, spice or lavender in the centre of each circle of material, and tie tightly with wool.
5. Fix each one onto the plait with another piece of wool and tie at the back. Spread out the gathers to make a fan shape.

12

illustrated by Chris Sheridan

Odd as a Haddock

by Agnes Szudek

illustrated by Shelagh McGee

Monday was always a day of panic at Miss Browbeater's Academy. A new week brought new problems. As my story begins, the teacher of Junior 1 had just telephoned to say she was going to the dentist and would be out all day. Miss Browbeater's main panic was at the thought of spending a whole day with boisterous Junior 1.

"Iris?" she called to her secretary in the adjoining room. "Ring the education office. I must have a supply teacher immediately. And don't take 'no' for an answer."

Iris appeared at the door. "Yes, Miss Browbeater. No, Miss Browbeater."

She hurried back to her telephone and returned a few moments later to say, "They haven't got a teacher to spare, headmistress."

"Not one to spare? Surely there must be someone in need of a bob-a-job. Try them again, Iris."

Iris hesitated. "Well, they'll ring back, because there *might* just be one, although she's tricky to get hold of. They did suggest a pigeon – "

"A pigeon? They must be mad! A lion-tamer would hardly be adequate for that class. No, Iris, I will not be fobbed off with a pigeon."

"But I didn't mean – "

The telephone rang, putting an end to this conversation. It was the education office. "We can help, after all," said the voice at the end of the line. "There's only one, though. It's take-it-or-leave-it, I'm afraid."

"I only want one," said Miss Browbeater, impatiently. "But certainly not a pigeon, you understand."

"This one doesn't teach much nowadays," the voice went on, ignoring the pigeon remark. "Wanders about a lot, but she's in the district at the moment. The name's Bodella Peep. A bit odd mind you, but willing once she's caught."

"Bodella Peep. Oh, she can be as odd as a haddock, so long as she comes – and quickly." Miss Browbeater put down the receiver.

"Bodella Peep, Bodella Peep. What a strange name," murmured Iris, who was awaiting further instructions.

"Mind your own business, Iris Thistlewart. We can't all have grand-sounding names. Back to your desk please, or you'll have the dinner-money in on top of you before you're ready."

The headmistress collected an armful of books and, on reflection, opened her cupboard and took out a ball of stout string and a pair of knitted bootees. "Just in case they're troublesome," she said, thoughtfully, and marched off in the direction of the Junior 1 classroom.

She was far from ready when the children bundled in and took their places. And, by the time she had called the register, given out books, rulers and pencils, the bell rang for play-time. It was much the same after play and hardly any work had been done before it was time for dinner.

Exhausted with the demands of forty seven-year-olds, Miss Browbeater clawed her way along the corridor to her office. She had no sooner called for a cup of tea and collapsed into her chair, when she jumped up again at a loud *honk! honk!* outside the window.

"Oh, those dashed geese from the farm! They're in the playground again. If they can't be kept under control, they should be shot. Iris? Iris?"

On the tail of Miss Browbeater's words came half a dozen loud reports like gun-shot. "Oh, no, I didn't really mean it," she wailed. "I didn't want him to. Oh, the heartless farmer!"

Iris hurried over to the window and looked out. "No, no, it's not geese at all," she said. "It's Miss Peep, by the look of things. She's come in a sort of – motor."

It *was* Miss Bodella Peep, on top of a very ancient, high, motor-car that was wide open everywhere. The motor trembled to a stop, shuddered, groaned, and down from it stepped the supply teacher.

Her white hair was fluffed about her head like untamed mohair. She wore layers of garments, all different lengths, as though she carried her entire wardrobe on her back. Over her arms hung three large, bulging carpet-bags with tassels swinging at the ends. She carried a gold-beaded handbag and around her neck were binoculars and a field flask.

"Here we are, darlings!" she called to the playground in general. The children, waiting for their school dinners, stopped playing and rushed to surround the strange-looking newcomer. "Here today, gone tomorrow! What clever children you are. I can tell by the look of you." She spoke in a warm, dithery voice. "Now, *shoo-shoo*! Play away and let me get myself arranged, arranged. Then we'll have a zipping time together."

But the children clustered about her all the more until Miss Browbeater came to the rescue. "What a blessing you were in the district, Miss Peep. Welcome!" She offered her hand with relief. "The education office said at first there was no hope."

"No, hope, hope? What twaddle-waddle! They've got my pigeon, haven't they? Peep's Special Carrier. That bird could find me in a pothole, and they know it. But, I must admit," she said, impishly, "sometimes I don't want to be found, especially in the wool-gathering season, you know."

"Wool-gathering?" queried Miss Browbeater.

"But of course. I tend to get into spots of bother then." Miss Peep patted one of the carpet-bags. "Straight from the hedges, straight from the ditches; faster than fairies, faster than witches. Oh, I go at quite a rate, if I'm left in peace, peace."

Miss Browbeater had tried and failed to keep up with this information. "Quite," she said. "Junior 1 classroom is at the far end of the corridor. Iris will bring you tea or coffee before lunch if you wish."

"No tea. No coffee. No lunch." Miss Peep's cheeks wobbled like half-set jellies as she shook her head. "I carry a flask of my Peep's Special Brew. It is health-giving, energy-giving and patience-giving." She called this over her shoulder as she walked away.

Miss Browbeater walked backwards as she gazed after the peculiar figure trudging along the corridor with bags and garments swinging from side to side, and goloshes that squelched as if they carried water as well as feet. "Like a short-legged camel," the headmistress murmured, recalling a recent visit to the zoo.

Bodella Peep may have looked eccentric and untidy, but she was organised and ready for Junior 1 when they came in after dinner. She had no discipline worries because all the children she had ever taught were so fascinated by her appearance that they could not take their eyes off her, even for a brief moment's mischief.

Miss Peep looked over her spectacles with outstretched neck and said, "I can tell by the way you're sitting that you're not too sure of your eight-times table, table. That's where we'll

begin. Now, sit up, eyes on me, and no pranks, my darlings."

With incredible speed, she wrote the eight-times table on the blackboard, each number perfectly formed, clear and beautiful. She then took a small polished stick from her gold-beaded bag and pulled it out like a telescope. Its end was like a shepherd's crook. "Are we ready?" she asked, pointing to the board. "All together now. Ready, steady, go."

The class began:

> "One eight is eight,
> Two eights are sixteen,
> Three eights are twenty-four,
> Four eights are thirty-two,
> Five eights are forty-one – "

"Stop! Stop!" cried Miss Peep in horror. "Forty-one? Forty-one? No, no, five eights are forty, forty. The very number in the class. So easy to remember. Again, from the top."

The children began again and again, but each time they came to five eights, they said, "Forty-one," until Miss Peep became annoyed.

"Why, you're not even trying. It seems to me you're nothing more than a flock of sheep, sheep, all following blindly without thinking." She banged her crook on the blackboard. "Now, properly, if you please."

Junior 1 started yet again, but it was a very different sound that Miss Peep heard:

> "Meh, meh, me-meh,
> Meh, meh, me-meh-meh . . ."

She turned round slowly, her eyes closed, but when she opened them, she saw exactly what she feared. Sitting before her, their hooves propped up on the desks, were forty grey woolly sheep. Too late, she had used the forbidden word in the wool-gathering season. Sheep meant sheep when that rare crook was in her hand. Miss Peep's name was no accident or joke. Her great, great, great grandmother had been Bo-Peep the first, after whom she had been named.

"Sheep, sheep! I've done it again!" she cried, quivering all over. "I knew I should have stayed hidden away a little longer. Silly me! I'll never learn. Oh, the poor darlings!"

Afraid the headmistress might come along, Miss Peep looked into the corridor. It was empty. Beckoning to the nearest sheep, she ushered it out of the door and like all good sheep, the others followed. But once outside, the sheep began to bleat, jostle and trot about like a farmyard mutiny. Within seconds, Miss Browbeater appeared.

"Great heavens! How ghastly!" she shouted above the racket. "It's that careless farmer again. His livestock takes advantage of the

entire countryside. First his geese, now his sheep. But don't worry, Miss Peep, I'll soon have them shifted." She strode away, fuming, as Bodella Peep raised her arms in despair.

"Junior 1, shifted?" She clutched three of her cardigans at once, and turned nervously to her flock. "This is disastrous, my darlings. Now listen carefully. You are to be good little sheep and wait until I bring you home, wagging your tails behind you, so to speak." She patted one or two curly heads and slip-slopped back to the classroom.

There she searched frantically in her gold-beaded bag, but could not find what she was looking for. Finally, she slung the bag over her arm together with the three carpet-bags and looked out of the window.

Along the narrow country road came the farmer in his land-rover, with two black and white sheep dogs. But when he saw the sheep, he was not keen to move them. Bodella Peep held her breath and listened.

"They're not mine," said the farmer after looking some of the animals straight in the eye. "I know my sheep and my sheep know me. This lot's strange to these parts."

Miss Browbeater's voice rose to its most ferocious. "Strangers? Rubbish, man!" she shrieked. "Your fields come right up to the school wall. Of course they're yours. Where d'you think they came from – Ramsgate? Get them off school premises this minute, before I call the police."

"Ah, you're wrong, m'dear," said the farmer, patiently. "I knows me onions and me sheep, but just to please you, I'll run them into the small field up the hill and if they're not claimed, I'll get them off to market in the morning."

"To market?" whispered Miss Peep, still at the window. "Not if I can help it. I've got to sort them out before three-thirty." She waited until the flock had been herded up to the small field where the two dogs were left on guard. When she was satisfied that Miss Browbeater was safely back in her office, Bodella Peep, half-crouching, half-crawling, squelched her way up the hill.

She hid under a low-spreading oak tree and again began rummaging in her small bag. "I know I've got it somewhere. I'm never without it. Oh, where is it?" She pulled out a mirror, tweezers, a magnifying-glass and other odds and ends, but still could not find the vital object. In exasperation, she tipped the bag upside-down on the grass. "Got it!" she cried, pouncing on a small shiny acorn.

It was not one from the tree under which she was sitting. This one was as highly polished as her telescopic crook and its top opened on a tiny brass hinge. Inside was a scrap of ancient-looking cloth, flimsy as cobweb.

Bodella Peep took the tweezers, carefully unrolled the fabric and, peering through her magnifying-glass, began to read:

"The man who first shall pass your way,
Must stop and clearly to you say:
Bodella Peep, Bodella Peep, pray
Have you any wool today?

Though you be taken for a fool,
Your answer must be firm and cool:
Why yes, sir, why yes, sir,
I've three bags full.

"Of course, it's so simple. How could I forget?" she smiled, before realising that the only man she was likely to meet on that lonely hillside was the farmer, and she couldn't let him know what had happened. Time was running out. The sheep were bleating anxiously in the background when a loud holler made Bodella Peep squeak with shock.

"Peek-a-boo-hoo!" a rough voice croaked behind her. She turned and saw the weatherbeaten face of a thin man grinning at her round the tree trunk. As he came fully into view, she saw that his clothes were ragged, from his cloth cap to the broken soles of his boots.

"My dear fellow," Miss Peep said, scrambling to her knees. "Oh, my dear fellow."

"Never been called that 'afore," said the man, grinning some more. He raised his cap and bowed, almost to the grass. "Jack-the-tramp, that's me."

"Bodella Peep, that's me, in a frightful muddle," said Bodella Peep, thinking how long it must have been since he had washed his face.

"Then allow me, your ladyship." The tramp dropped to the grass, his knees clicking like nutcrackers, and began to pick up the odds and ends.

"Oh, no, not these," said Miss Peep hastily. "It's the sheep. All I want you to do is to ask me a question. It's very simple."

But Jack-the-tramp backed away, still on his knees. "What question?" he asked cagily.

Miss Peep thrust her magnifying-glass into the man's grubby fingers and held the scrap of cloth on the palm of her hand. "Read this," she instructed, pointing to the words.

Fortunately the tramp had been to school somewhere and could read. "Bodella Peep, Bodella Peep, pray have you any wool today? Will that do?" he asked.

Miss Peep nodded her head vigorously, opened each of her bulging bags of sheep's wool and her warm, dithery voice sang across the countryside:

> "Why yes, sir, why yes, sir,
> I've three bags full.
> None for the master,
> None for the dame;
> They're all for the children
> To bring them back again."

At once the sheep began to dissolve and, as if they had beamed down from space, the children gradually appeared. They came tumbling and leaping over the gate without waiting to open it. The sheep dogs flattened their ears and fled in fear at the pounding legs while Jack-the-tramp plunged wildly down the hillside shouting, "Oh, Jack be nimble, Jack be quick," and other fading mumbles.

Junior 1 ran to Bodella Peep, all yelling together. "We've had a terrific time! Like being in another world. You're a real wizard, Miss Peep!"

"Hush! Don't say that!" Bodella Peep held up her hands in horror. "Never say that! Right, into a snappy crocodile, quickly. The bell's going to ring any minute."

Miss Browbeater was standing in the yard as the tame, smiling crocodile walked through the school gate. She glowed with pride at the perfect behaviour of her most rumbustious pupils and said, "Ah-ha! Been out for a nature ramble, I see?"

Miss Peep smiled sweetly. "It's amazing what one can come across in the wool-gathering season," she said, and set about cranking her motor.

As she climbed up on to her vehicle, the children begged her to come again, but Miss Peep made no promises. "Here today, gone tomorrow, darlings," she called, and waved goodbye, smacking kisses into the air. The old motor-car rattled away in a cloud of dust and smoke with the occasional report like gun-shot.

Back in her office, Miss Browbeater turned to Iris Thistlewart. "She may be as odd as a *couple* of haddocks, but what a teacher! Her handling of Junior 1 was sheer magic! We'll try to get hold of her again when she's in the district – in the wool-gathering season, of course."

Lockwood Donkey Sanctuary

GIRL GUIDES

photographs by Tony Rose

The Lockwood Home of Rest for Old and Sick Donkeys was started many years ago by John and Kay Lockwood to provide a home for old and unwanted donkeys. Many of the original donkeys brought to the sanctuary had worked in pits and quarries and would have been destroyed when they were too old or sick to work any longer, but John and Kay felt that these donkeys deserved a happier prospect, and decided to give them the chance to live out their final years in peace and safety.

Nowadays most of the donkeys are bought at auctions or given by people who are unable to keep them any longer.

This donkey, Lucy, is very special. Several years ago she injured her right hind leg, and usually when this happens to a horse, pony or donkey, they have to be put to sleep. Lucy was very lucky because doctors at the Roehampton Hospital decided to see whether Lucy could be fitted with an artificial leg. As you can see from the picture, this was a success and now Lucy is quite famous as the only donkey in the world with a 'wooden' leg (actually it is made of fibreglass).

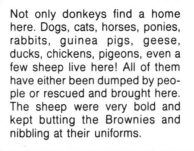

Not only donkeys find a home here. Dogs, cats, horses, ponies, rabbits, guinea pigs, geese, ducks, chickens, pigeons, even a few sheep live here! All of them have either been dumped by people or rescued and brought here. The sheep were very bold and kept butting the Brownies and nibbling at their uniforms.

This little black lamb had to be bottle-fed by Mrs Lockwood as its mother was unable to feed it.

The Brownies of the 1st Whitley Pack are frequent visitors to the Donkey Home.

Situated in Wormley, near Godalming, the Home (which is open to the public) relies entirely on donations and legacies to sur-vive. Visitors can 'adopt' a donkey for a small fee, and several of the Brownies had done this on a pre-vious occasion.

TOYS FOR YOUR DELIGHT

GIRL GUIDES

What is your oldest toy? Perhaps you have a doll or teddy bear that belonged to an older sister, or your Mum, or even your Granny. If you go to the Museum of Childhood, in Edinburgh, you can see toys that belonged to children centuries ago. I visited the museum with the 211th City of Edinburgh Brownie Pack, and we spent the afternoon looking at all the different things on display.

I met the Brownies at the City of Edinburgh Guide Headquarters in Melville Street.

On the way to the museum we walked through the famous gardens on Princes Street.

photographs by Norman Redfern

Across the gardens, and up above us we could see Edinburgh Castle.

The museum is on Edinburgh's Royal Mile, which runs between the castle and Holyrood Palace. It was the first museum in the world to be devoted solely to the history of childhood.

Inside there are not only toys, but clothes, books, school desks, all sorts of things that children would have used or played with. These Brownies are looking at a collection of badges.

There are many old games on display, including card games.

This doll, called 'my dream baby', was made in the 1920s in Germany. The oldest baby doll in the museum was made in the eighteenth century and is very fragile.

These two Brownies found some old books about Guides. Lesley, on the left, is reading *The Girl Scout,* first published in 1913, and Gillian is reading *The Oakhill Guide Company,* published in 1933.

This magnificent dolls' house was made in the late eighteenth century and is based on a real house in Kent. Many of the items inside are original, but subsequent owners added extra furnishings and fitments and now the house even has electric lights and running water.

The back of the house comes off completely so you can see right inside.

This marionette had only just arrived at the museum. Like most of the toys, it was sent as a gift. It had not yet been put on display, but the curator, John Hay, allowed the Brownies to look at it.

This Guide uniform had also just arrived in the post. Mr Hay was not certain how old it was, and asked my advice.

This model kitchen was made by the 1st Logie Brownie Pack, Forth Valley, for a dolls' house competition run by the museum and the Save the Children Fund. Some of the winning entries are on display in the museum.

Mr Hay told the Brownies that the museum opened in 1955 and since then has built up such a large collection of exhibits (over 40,000) that they have run out of space to display them. However, they are planning to take over the premises next door, which will double the area of the museum.

On the way back to Guide Headquarters we stopped at the castle.

Penny Mor

STRANGE PETS

There can hardly be a single one of you who hasn't at some time or other owned a pet of some kind, a cat, dog, rabbit, mouse, tortoise, hamster, or maybe a budgie. Those of you who live in the country may even have owned a special pet such as a pony.

However, looking back into history, you can find some very strange animals that have been kept as pets.

Florence Nightingale owned a little owl which she loved dearly and took everywhere with her in her pocket. She called the owl Athena because she had bought it in Athens while on holiday.

She came across the owl when she saw some children throwing stones at something; when she looked more closely she found it was a fluffy young owlet which had fallen from its nest in a tree.

She managed to stop the children tormenting the bird and gave them some money for it.

Athena became devoted to Florence and would sit on her head, eat out of her hand, and play with her by hiding behind books in her library at home, swooping down on visitors unexpectedly. The owl had its own favourite armchair on which it perched, and would dare anyone to move it from there by staring at them in a most threatening way.

King Charles II was utterly devoted to dogs, and his court was dominated by special spaniels which were later named King Charles Spaniels. His Queen also had her favourite dogs which everyone at court called 'Small Ladyes Poppees'.

King Charles had a lot of trouble with his dogs, which always seemed to be getting lost. On one occasion he even advertised for the return of one: 'A lost dog. No doubt stolen or strayed. Belonging to His Majesty'.

Queen Elizabeth I, who loved fine clothes and

jewellery, had most appropriate pets – peacocks! She loved them because they always appeared so proud and elegant in their lovely colours. They were allowed to strut around her court in complete freedom so that she could watch them displaying their beautiful tail feathers.

The fashion of owning strange and curious pets was often started by sailors who would bring back animals and birds from far-off countries.

At one time it was the fashion for rich people to own young crocodiles and they would lead them around the streets of London and other cities on special golden chains. Although many people were charmed when they first saw these small crocodiles, they soon feared them, as they grew larger, and they ceased to be kept as pets.

In Paris one pet fancier, Baroness de

Berckheim, loved tortoises so much that she would take them with her whenever she visited friends. When she went to the park for a stroll she would take the tortoises with her for some exercise, and she would get them all to go in the same direction by prodding them with a large walking stick which she carried.

Another member of the French nobility, Princess de Lucinge, always appeared to have a lap dog on her knees at court, until some of her friends looked more closely and realised she was actually pampering a lion cub!

Her sister had similarly strange ideas about what made a suitable pet. She was well known in Paris by the fact that she took a black goat with her whenever she left her mansion!

Yet another French lady of the eighteenth century, Mademoiselle Fournier-Sarlovez, had perhaps the strangest pet of all. She went about trailing a long black thread behind her, and many people were totally mystified by it. However, closer inspection showed that at the end of the thread was her particular pet, a black beetle!

Monkeys were popular with everyone when they were first brought to this country by sailors, and both rich and poor people kept them. They were easily taught to do tricks of all sorts, and it was quite common to see monkeys perched on the shoulders of adults and children. Some monkeys were very mischievous, and when they jumped and swung around in people's kitchens and living rooms they caused damage and ill-feeling, and so became less popular as pets.

At one time, children living in the countryside would go out into the fields and catch small crickets. They would put them into special baskets which they hung beneath the windows of their homes. Everyone thought it was lovely to wake up in the morning to the cheerful sound of the crickets chirping in the baskets.

An Italian poet, Gabriele d'Annuzio, kept a large number of snakes as pets. It's said that he kept as many as forty of them in a large cage outside his house to frighten away the many people who came to his house asking him to settle his debts with them.

Agnes Baden-Powell, sister of our Founder, Lord Baden-Powell, kept bees. You may think this is not unusual, but she kept them *inside* her house. They lived in a glass hive and found their way in and out through a pipe laid in the wall. Agnes won several prizes in competitions for her honey. She also had a colony of butterflies living in her house, and in the hall small birds flew about.

In the past many people, especially those who were rich, kept unusual pets to keep themselves amused, as they were often bored. But today pets are much more important because they are real companions to many people. We really love our pets, choosing them carefully, and looking after them well. Pets teach us to be kind to animals, and we must never forget that they need our constant protection and affection during their whole life from the moment that we decide to adopt them.

John Oliver

illustrated by Belinda Lyon

Puzzles

Who Am I?

by Niva Miles

I have a saddle
But I'm not a horse,
No ears to hear,
I'm deaf of course.

I live in a burrow,
But no rabbit I,
I'm blind as a bat,
And cannot fly.

No legs and no nose,
So you might suppose
I'm useless.

But, I can dig
Though I'm not a spade.
I'm the farmer's friend
And the gardener's aid.

I'm long and thin,
With bristles too.
Of course you know me.
Guess who!

Pantomime Puzzle

by Ann Hillyer

The Jester's Badge is fun to work for. How much do you know about Pantomimes? In which Pantomimes do the following appear?

1. A hen, a plant and a very big, fierce man?
2. A mirror and a poisoned apple?
3. A wicked uncle and a lamp?
4. A cat, a ship and the sound of Bow Bells?
5. A pumpkin and a prince?
6. A spinning wheel and a bad fairy?

Answers are on page 61.

Some jobs are very popular. Everyone enjoys taking the scraps down to the pig-bin, because we take turns to ride in the trek cart.

We all help with the washing-up after every meal, but even that seems fun when the weather's nice and we can do it outside.

Another thing about Pack Holiday is that although we don't camp, we spend as much time as we possibly can out-of-doors. Help-yourself salad in the garden was one of our favourite meals.

What else is special about Pack Holiday?
Well, we all help to choose a theme
or story for the week.
Brown Owl hoped ours would
be E.T., but we chose Winnie the Pooh!

Having a theme makes the holiday really special. For a whole week we live the story. Here we are making bees, like the ones that chased Pooh.

Some of us made Piglet money-boxes — in fact everything we made came out of the story.

Every afternoon, something really exciting happens. After lunch Brown Owl reads us a bit of the story, to give us a clue what we are going to do.

Then we have a rest, but all the time we are wondering what is going to happen when we get up.

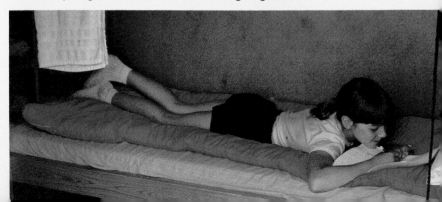

One afternoon, we found ourselves hunting the Woozle. Here we are taking a compass bearing to find out which way he went!

Another day, we all searched for the Horrible Heffalump. We followed the lumps of honey he'd dropped all through the forest.

When we got back to the house the Heffalump was lurking, ready to jump out and try to catch us. Some of the younger ones didn't realise it was only Brown Owl!

But the best thing of all about a Pack Holiday is that it's like a Brownie Meeting that goes on for a whole week. No wonder it's the best Venture of all!

Games Granny Played

by Alan Major

"What shall we play now?" I expect you say that often when you are with your friends and don't know what to do next. But did it ever occur to you that your mother and grandmother probably said it just as often as you do, when they were your age? "I know," someone would say excitedly, "let's play . . ."

Well, what did they play?

You might think tracking is a modern game, devised by Brown Owl to improve your skills of observation, but children were playing it at the beginning of this century, and for many centuries before that. The children would divide into two teams, those who would lay the trail of clues, and those who would follow them. Sometimes it was agreed beforehand what the clues would be, such as scraps of paper attached to twigs, or under stones, or arrows made of sticks or stones.

In town this tracking game was sometimes called 'Chalk Chase' and the trail layers would use chalk to make a mark for the seekers to find. Sometimes the trail layers would make a false trail, sending the followers off in the wrong direction. At the end of the false trail there would be a cross to tell the seekers they had to go back and start again!

The correct trail would lead to the hiding place of the trail layers, where they would be waiting, hoping to escape detection. Sometimes they would leave a clue for the seekers to show they were getting close, usually an H for Home, or F for Find.

There are a great many hiding games that children played in the past and still play today. Probably the most popular is 'Hide and Seek', which was even played a thousand years ago by children in Ancient Greece! There are many different rules for this game, but the most usual way to play is for all the girls but one to hide and stay there until they are discovered, the first one to be found being the seeker in the next game.

A game that your grandmothers probably played is Drophandkerchief. In this all but one of the girls forms a large circle sitting on the ground, or standing facing inwards. The girl who is 'out' runs round the outside of the circle singing, "I sent a letter to my love and on the way I dropped it; one of you has picked it up and put it in her pocket." Then she drops a handkerchief behind one of the girls in the circle and runs on round the ring. Whoever has the handkerchief dropped behind her has to pick it up and run in the opposite direction around the circle to try and get back to her place before the girl who is 'out' reaches it. Whoever is last to reach the place is 'out' next time round. Sometimes when this is played the girl going round taps the head of each girl as she passes, saying, "No, not you, no, not you," until she reaches the girl she has chosen to race; then she says, "But you!"

Another chasing game that was popular a hundred years ago, and is still very popular in a slightly different form, is 'What's the time, Mr Wolf?' Originally it was called 'Fox and Chickens' or 'Fox and Hens'. One player is the fox and the others a hen and her chicks. The hen follows the fox around asking the time. The fox says all different times of the day, and continues walking until it is, "Twelve o'clock at night!" at which point the fox turns and chases the hen and chickens.

'Feet-off-ground' is another game your grandmother might have played. It is a chase game, where you cannot be caught if you have your feet off the ground, by standing on a wall, large stone, sitting on a fence, or similar. A variation is to have one special place where you are safe, such as a box to stand on, but two people may not stand on it at once.

When a rest was needed in a game to get your breath back, it was quite common in your grandmother's day to say, "Feighnights." You had to cross your first two fingers and stand on one leg, or maybe stand on a wall. While doing this you could not be caught. This word is very old and has been used by children to ward off pursuers for over six hundred years. It comes from the phrase "fain I", or "feign I" which was a way of asking to be excused from a particular job or task.

I wonder which of the games you play will still be played when *your* granddaughters are Brownies?

illustrated by Stanley Houghton 41

43

This year the Girl Guides Association is 75 years old. That is a great age — rather the same as being a great-grandmother or grandfather. In 1910, the year Guiding began, you will be surprised to learn that there were no such people as Brownies, though I expect there were a lot of girls *wanting* to be Brownies if only Brownies had existed. However, they had to wait until 1914 when they were allowed to be Rosebuds. Very soon they changed their name to Brownies and wore a brown uniform not so very different from yours, though I do not think you would like to wear the hat very much!

But if the uniform was not so very different, everything else was. You most probably would have had very long hair tied with enormous ribbons, or worn in plaits, which is why the early Brownies had to know how to plait. Your clothes were usually made of quite thick material, with a large number of petticoats, and they reached down below the knee — hopeless for playing games or running about in. Even if you were lucky enough to go to the seaside you certainly would not have been allowed to wear shorts or sandals or anything as comfortable as that, while the bathing suits were rather extraordinary, as you can see from the picture.

If you had lived in a big town you would have found that people were still driving about in horse-drawn carriages or omnibuses, though there were electric trams (rather like old-fashioned trains) running on metal rails through the streets, and a few motor taxis and private motor cars. There were no zebra crossings, however, no parking meters, and certainly no traffic lights. Nor were there any speed limit signs because motor cars only went very slowly.

For entertainment you might have played hopscotch, or bowled a hoop, and you would most probably have had a great many brothers and sisters to play with, because families were usually larger then. Perhaps your mother or father played a musical instrument, in which case the whole family would join in singing songs. There was no television for you to watch and no record players on which to listen to your favourite music. You probably would not even have had a radio (it was called a wireless then). But you might have gone to the circus, watched a Punch and Judy show, listened to an open-air band or heard an organ-grinder playing, while his monkey performed amusing antics. Most of your fun, however, you would have made up for yourself.

I think you would have found shopping very different as well. Have you gone with your mother or father to a supermarket and helped to push a big trolley up and down the store? Well, there were no such things as supermarkets in those days. Most shops were small, and sold only one kind of product. Frequently they had chairs by the counters so that you could sit down while waiting for your purchase to be wrapped. As for the sweet

shops – I think you would have loved them, with their rows and rows of enormous glass jars filled to the brim with sweets. One new penny in today's money would have bought a great many sweets then. They had no paper wrapping so you could pop them straight into your mouth – but even in those days sweets were not very good for your teeth, so Brownies were expected to know how to clean their teeth, and why. The milkman delivered milk to your door, but not in today's milk bottles and not on a milk float. He usually came round in a horse-driven cart, with the milk in churns (see the picture). The milk was put in the coolest part of the house, usually the pantry, because there were no fridges. Sometimes men might come to your door selling their wares, and your mother might buy onions, perhaps, or ribbon, or have her knives sharpened by them. Nobody ordered things by telephone because only the very, very rich had telephones, so think how important it was then for a Brownie to be able to carry a message correctly in her head.

When it grew dark, if you lived in a town your house might have been lit by gaslight, but I doubt if it would have had electric light. Sometimes in the country they still used candles. There was no central heating in houses, so you would have been glad of your warm clothes. The only way to make your house warm was to have open fires. These were lovely to look at, but an awful lot of hard work to lay and light. One of the tests for early Brownies was to know how to lay and light a fire, and you can see how important it must have been to be able to do this. Helping at home, as every Brownie tries to do, was much harder in those days because there were so few machines to make housework easier. Vacuum cleaners had just been invented, but the early ones were so huge that they had to be drawn up outside the house on a cart, and clean the house from there! If you burned a saucepan it was much harder to clean because there were no such things as non-stick saucepans, yet the early Brownies had to try to make a milk pudding, and I expect you all know how difficult it is to clean anything when the milk boils over!

School was different as well, and though it varied from place to place, you could quite easily have left when you were twelve, which didn't give you very much time to learn things. There weren't as many exciting things to do at school, either, and certainly not as many games, so it is not surprising that when Lord Baden-Powell invented Guiding, the biggest game of all, younger sisters were soon clamouring to be allowed to join in.

Tin Forbes

French knitting
— with a difference

by Rosemary Dines

If you've already learnt to do French knitting, you probably used either a special gadget which you bought as part of a kit, or perhaps someone found you an old wooden cottonreel and fixed four nails into it for you to use.

You can actually learn to French knit without either of these things. Here's what you need:

One spring-type clothes peg
Some double knitting wool

1. First, tie one end of the wool round one 'prong' of the clothes peg and fasten with a knot.

2. Now wind the wool round the other prong to make a figure eight.

3. Make another figure eight by winding the wool round both prongs again then lift the bottom loop on each prong over the top loop and the prong. Pull the spare end of the wool gently.

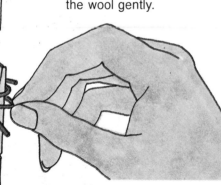

4. Now keep doing step 3 until your knitting is as long as you want it.

Things to make with your knitting

Mats: make different coloured chains and stick them onto a card base.

Pendant: thread garden wire through the centre and bend into a shape. Add a loop and thread onto a cord.

Egg cosy: stitch your knitting – carefully! – round an egg to get the shape right. Make a woolly pom-pom to go on top using two circles of card 3 cm (1¼″) across.

illustrated by Chris Sheridan

The Grand Pet Show

by Howard Tennant

illustrated by Val Sangster

Janice Hudson is daft. I know she's my best friend, but there's no getting away from it. In fact, when you think about it, all the Hudsons must be daft: Mr Hudson, Mrs Hudson, Peter, Wendy, and last of all, Janice. I mean, who ever heard of anyone having a zoo in the middle of a city like ours? Well, my dad calls it a zoo.

Their house is only the same size as ours: three bedrooms, three rooms downstairs including the kitchen, and a backyard, and yet they've got more animals than sense, my mum says. You should hear my mum if I mention any of Janice's pets.

"Ridiculous, I call it. Who on earth in their right minds would have all those animals in a house like that? It's not as if they've got a garden. That house must smell, it really must. And it must cost them a fortune in food. What do they do when they go on holiday? They can't take them all with them." Then she folds her arms and gives me one of her looks, just like she did when I asked if we could look after two of Janice's pets while they went on holiday to Blackpool. I didn't tell her until they were safely in my bedroom and the Hudsons well on their way to Blackpool, that the pets were Flash and Gordon, Janice's pet rats. Mum said I had to keep my bedroom tidy all week because she was not going into a room with rats in it, caged or not. It's a good job Flash and Gordon didn't hear her, because they are easily upset. They'd have sulked all week.

I suppose really I ought to tell you just how many pets the Hudsons have got. I'll have to think carefully though, because there are so many. Well, Mr Hudson has his pigeons, dozens of them, and you never see him anywhere without Sam his dog. Mrs Hudson has two cats, Marmalade and Ginger, and she also has a large tank of tropical fish. Peter has a couple of female gerbils, Salt and Pepper, and Wendy has a rabbit and a guinea pig, Hazel and Clapton. Janice has Flash and Gordon of course, and she also has a couple of budgies, Joey and Rocky Two. (Rocky One went to live with Janice's Aunty Elsie in Wigan.) I think that's all of them.

You can imagine the look on Janice's face when Brown Owl announced that as part of our Animal Week (when we were raising money for the R.S.P.C.A.) we would hold a Grand Pet Show on the Friday evening.

"I do hope most of you will be entering your pet in the show," Brown Owl said. "Do tell all your friends. I want this to be the best pet show Clayton has ever seen."

As soon as we had sung Brownie Bells I ran over to the Gnomes. I'm in the Pixies.

"Ooh! Janice, which of your pets are you going to bring?"

"I don't know, Adele," she said. "Flash and Gordon are not everybody's cup of tea, so I suppose I'll bring Joey or Rocky Two."

We met Wendy on her way home from Guides

and told her about the pet show.

"I'll have to show Hazel, my rabbit," she said, "because Clapton has an eye infection. It sounds great. I can't wait." Neither could we.

On the Monday of Animal Week we held a jumble sale and Janice and I were helping on the toy stall. We raised nearly eight pounds, but Janice did not seem too pleased.

"What's up, Janice?" I said.

"Joey and Rocky Two are moulting, you know, losing some of their feathers. They look awful. I can't take them to the show on Friday."

"Well, take Flash and Gordon," I said.

"It wouldn't be fair on them," she replied. "They're both getting old and they've only just settled down again after staying with you while we were in Blackpool."

"Not to worry," I said. "My dad says your house is like a zoo. You've still got plenty of animals to take. Not like me. The only pet we've got is Tigger, our cat."

"I suppose you're right," she said. "Come on. They'll all be in for supper so I'll ask now."

We ran to Janice's house as quickly as we could. As we walked into the back room Mr Hudson was the first to see us. He dropped his paper on top of Sam, who was stretched out on the floor beside Mr Hudson's chair.

"Hey up! Here comes trouble! What can we do for you two young ladies?" he said in his usual smiling way. "I hope you don't want to borrow a fiver!"

"Dad," said Janice slowly. "Can I take Sam to the Pet Show on Friday?"

"What time on Friday?" her Dad asked.

"From six-thirty to seven-thirty."

"I'm sorry, love, you can't. I'm taking my pigeons to Carlisle on Friday and you know Sam wouldn't miss a trip out with the pigeons."

It was true. Wherever Mr Hudson went with his pigeons, Sam went too. Seems daft to me. Fancy taking those poor pigeons all that way and then making them fly back on their own! I wonder how they find their way back?

Janice turned to her mum, who was doing some ironing. You could tell that Mrs Hudson knew what was coming next, but she carried on with the ironing.

"Mum, do you think I could . . ."

"Why yes, of course, love. You can take Marmalade. She'd love to be in a show. She's a real show-off. You couldn't take the fish anyway. That tank weighs a ton. And I don't think Ginger would fancy it."

She was right. Ginger, their big tom-cat, was his own boss. He came and went as he pleased. He was also a bully, and was always going off chasing other cats. Sometimes, Janice said, he went off for days and days.

On Wednesday, Brown Owl had sent us out on a Treasure Hunt, with all the clues about animals. Janice and I were trotting down Field Street when we met Mrs Hudson.

"Oh, Janice," Mrs Hudson said. "I'm just on my way to bingo, but I hoped I might see you. I've got good news and bad news."

"Oh heck," said Janice. "What now?"

"Marmalade is going to have kittens. It must be soon because she's climbed into our wardrobe."

Janice looked at me. "She always goes in there a few days before she has her kittens."

She turned to her mum. "Don't worry, Mum. I know he won't win any prizes, but I can still take Ginger."

Mrs Hudson sighed. "That's the bad news, love. As I was coming out I saw our Ginger charging down Fourth Avenue after Mrs Wilson's Whiskers. He might be gone for days, and you know what a state he's in when he does come home."

I smiled to myself at the thought of Mrs Wilson having whiskers, but I could see Janice was not amused.

"Is your Peter showing Salt and Pepper? If he's not, you could take them."

"You never know with our Pete. It depends what sort of a mood he's in. Anyway, we'll see him later."

We waved goodbye to Mrs Hudson and then Janice looked at the list of clues. "A place for keeping cows leads to an animal lover."

"I don't understand it at all," she said.

I glanced up and noticed the name of the street we were on. Field Street. Then it became clear.

"Look," I said. "*Field* Street; a place for keeping cows. And what's at the end of Field Street?"

"Just St Francis' Primary School," said Janice. Then the penny dropped. "Of course, St Francis, an animal lover! Come on!"

When we reached the school, Brown Owl was waiting for us.

"Well done, you two. You're the first to reach this point." Then she noticed the look on Janice's face. "What's the matter, Janice?"

"Oh, Brown Owl! You know how many animals we've got! Well, it looks as if I won't have a pet to bring on Friday." She explained about all the pets and said that Peter was her last hope.

"Oh, I'm sure Peter will let you bring his gerbils. They're such lively little animals. He won't want to see you disappointed. Look, why don't you run to your house now and ask him? It's only round the corner, isn't it? You've got time to get there and back and still finish the Treasure Hunt."

We didn't wait, but ran all the way back to Janice's house. As Janice pushed open the back door we could hear Pete's voice.

"I don't believe it! It's impossible! It can't be! I just don't believe it!"

"Hi Janice, hello Adele. Hey, what do you think? You know those two female gerbils of mine? Well, come and look at this. But be quiet, I don't want to disturb them."

We followed Peter into the back room and he motioned to us to move slowly and put his finger to his lips. "Shhh . . ."

One of the gerbils was sitting in its food dish nibbling some seeds. The other was curled up on some cotton wool. I was just going to ask Peter why she was sitting on pink jelly babies when one of the jelly babies wriggled. They were alive. Baby gerbils.

"I thought Salt and Pepper were both females, Pete," I said.

"So did I," Peter replied. "Salt is. Pepper isn't. Come on, you two, gerbils don't like being disturbed when they've got young. I think I'll leave them alone for a few days."

Janice and I trooped out of the house. There was no need for her to ask Peter. The baby

gerbils meant that Janice now had no pet to take to the show on Friday.

We told Brown Owl the bad news.

"Well, you are unlucky, aren't you? What will you do now?"

"She can help me with Tigger, can't you, Janice?"

"I suppose so," said Janice. She didn't sound too keen.

As soon as Janice had finished her tea on Friday she came round to our house. We soon had Tigger looking better than he'd ever looked before. Without Janice, he would've looked just like any other cat, but she had seen her mother grooming Marmalade and was a real expert.

We carried Tigger in Marmalade's carrying basket. Even my mum said how smart he looked. When we arrived at the show the whole place was buzzing with noise and excitement. The cats were at the far end so we put Tigger in a spare show cage and had a look at the competition. After giving them all a good inspection Janice said she thought Tigger had a good chance of winning, but I could see she wasn't really excited. Here she was, animal-mad Janice Hudson at the first big pet show for ages, with no pet. Brown Owl came over and had a few words of sympathy for Janice.

Just then I saw Mrs Hudson at the other end of the room. When she saw us she came charging across.

"Cooee! Janice! Cooee! Hello, Mrs Colvin, hello Adele. Guess what, love! Marmalade has had her kittens. Three of them. They're lovely. Anyway, I'm on my way to bingo. I'll see you later. Oh dear, I nearly forgot! Before he left for Carlisle, your dad asked me to give this to you."

She handed Janice a little cardboard box tied with string, and darted away across the room.

Janice started to undo the string but the knots were too tight. My nails were longer so I untied the string for her, but I gave the box back so she could open it herself.

Inside was a little wooden cage and in one corner, cuddled up together, were two lovely little white mice.

"Oh, look, Adele!" Janice said excitedly. "Aren't they gorgeous?"

"They are pretty, aren't they?" said Brown Owl. "There's a piece of paper stuck on the bottom of the cage."

Janice pulled it off. It was from her dad.

"I couldn't see you going to the show empty-handed, so I got you these two at dinnertime. Love, Dad and Sam."

"You'd better go and find yourself a place with the other small cage animals, Janice," Brown Owl said.

Janice looked as if she thought it was a dream. She had a great big smile on her face as she moved away. As she was getting the mice ready a thought struck me. I wondered if the mice were both females. If not, the Hudson zoo would soon have even more new arrivals. I told you they were all daft, didn't I?

Our Houses

Did you know that as a member of the Girl Guides Association you own six houses? They are used as training centres for Guiders, and Guides and Rangers camp in the grounds. Some of them have special Pack Holiday houses for Brownies, too. I hope you will have the chance to visit some of our houses, if not as a Brownie, as a Guide; after all, they do belong to you!

Foxlease

This was the first house owned by the Girl Guides Association, given to us in 1922 by an American lady called Mrs Archbold. Our President at the time, the Princess Royal, gave the Association a large sum of money which had been given to her as a wedding present, to pay for the furnishing and upkeep of the house, which was re-named Princess Mary House, Foxlease.

Because Foxlease is in the New Forest, visitors get the chance to see plenty of wild life, including ponies and deer. Brownies can stay in Beaverbrook Lodge, the special Pack Holiday home, and if they are lucky, and the weather is fine, they may get the chance to swim in the beautiful outdoor pool.

Waddow Hall

Waddow Hall was bought by the Girl Guides Association in 1927 so that Guides living in the north of England could have their own training centre. The hall stands beside the river Ribble overlooking Pendle Hill, and Brownies, Guides and Rangers who visit Waddow can go for long walks in the Pennines or the Forest of Bowland.

There are seven camp sites, five cottages and a Pack Holiday house in the grounds, so many people can stay there.

Broneirion

Broneirion is the Welsh house, used by Guides Cymru. It was first lent to the Association in 1946 by Lady Davies, and has been used by Welsh Guides since 1947.

Just up the hill behind the house is 'Y Bwthyn Bach', the Brownie Pack Holiday home. In the Spring the bank in front of 'Y Bwthyn Bach' is covered with daffodils, the national flower of Wales.

In the dining room of the main house is some very special furniture. It was made by Robert Thompson, who carved his trademark, a little mouse, on each table and chair when it was finished. Brownies who visit Broneirion can have fun trying to spot all the mice!

Glenbrook

Glenbrook House, in the Peak District of Derbyshire, is our most recently acquired property, and is used mainly as a base for outdoor activities. Guides who camp at Glenbrook can go fell-walking and pony trekking, and Rangers can try many exciting activities, including potholing, archery, rock-climbing and canoeing.

Brownies who visit Glenbrook stay in the house and can go for interesting walks in the hills, or visit the nearby village of Bamford to watch sheep dog trials.

Netherurd

Among the heather-covered hills of Peebleshire, twenty-five miles south of Edinburgh, stands a handsome Georgian mansion. This is Netherurd, the house belonging to the Scottish Girl Guides. At first it was only rented to the Guides. The owner, Major E. G. Thomson, charged a rent of 2s 6d (12½p) a year! but in 1952 he gave it outright to the Association.

The Pack Holiday house was opened in 1956 as a memorial to Lady Thomson, sister-in-law of the Major, and County Commissioner for Peebleshire. Designed with Brownies in mind, all the kitchen fitments are at Brownie height.

Lorne

'Lorne Estate' is the official training centre for Guides in Northern Ireland. It was bought by the Girl Guides Association in 1946, and is our only house with a view of the sea. The grounds are divided by a ravine, through which flows a stream.

The house was built by a Scotsman, who named it after the ancient home of the Campbell clan, in Scotland. A Pack Holiday house was opened in 1963, called the Marion Greeves Brownie House. There are many trees in the grounds; over a thousand were planted in the winter of 1962/3!

Calling all Brownie Cooks!

As part of the celebrations for the 75th Anniversary of Guiding, Brownies, Guides and Rangers are going to try to do 75 Good Turns during Guide Week (June 24th–29th). I'm sure you will have many ideas for Good Turns in your Pack, but you can also do them individually. One idea is to make biscuits and cookies to sell for charity, or to give to people who would really appreciate them, perhaps an old lady or gentleman you know. You could also cook some as a contribution to your Pack's 75th Birthday Party, but do check with Brown Owl first in case she has other plans.

Don't forget to ask permission before you start cooking, and get someone to light the oven for you if it is needed. Put on your apron, tie back your hair, wash your hands, and you're ready to begin.

Brownies

75g/3oz margarine or butter
150g/6oz sugar
50g/2oz plain chocolate
2 eggs
75g/3oz self raising flour
a pinch of salt
50g/2oz shelled walnuts, chopped (if liked)

Method
Light oven Regulo 4, 180°C or 350°F

1. Grease a square 20 cm/8″ shallow tin with melted lard.
2. Put the butter and chocolate (broken into pieces) into a small saucepan. Melt them on a *low* heat, stirring with a wooden spoon.
3. When melted, remove the pan from the cooker and place carefully on a working surface. Pour in the sugar and mix in well, stirring until it has dissolved. Let the mixture stand to cool for a few minutes.
4. Break the eggs separately into a small basin and beat with a fork. Add each to the mixture in the pan and beat well.
5. Weigh and sift the flour and salt into a basin, then sift into the pan. Stir well.
6. If you are putting nuts in, add them next, stirring again.
7. Pour the mixture into the tin, smooth, and bake for 35–40 minutes until risen and shrinking from the sides of the tin. Cool in the tin, then cut into squares.

Coconut Crunchie

200g/8oz margarine (block)
125g/5oz sugar
75g/3oz desiccated coconut
50g/2oz cornflakes (crushed)
1 tablespoon cocoa
125g/5oz self raising flour

Method

Light oven Regulo 5, 190°C or 375°F.

1. Grease a swiss roll tin.
2. Weigh the sugar, coconut, cornflakes, cocoa and flour and mix together in a bowl.
3. Weigh and put the margarine into a small pan. Cut with a knife and then place on a low heat, stirring with a wooden spoon until it melts. Pour the melted margarine onto the dry ingredients and stir until well mixed.
4. Press firmly into the tin.
5. Bake in the oven for about 30 minutes.
6. Take from the oven and cut into pieces. Leave to cool in the tin. If you like, coat with melted chocolate before cutting. Wait until set before cutting.

Shortbread

150g/6oz plain flour
100g/4oz butter or margarine (softened)
50g/2oz sugar

Method
Light oven Regulo
3–4, 170–180°C or 325–350°F

1. Weigh the butter and sugar into a mixing bowl and beat hard with a wooden spoon until soft and pale in colour (creaming).
2. Weigh the flour into a bowl and sift into the creamed mixture a little at a time, stirring it until the flour has all been added. Continue until there is no dry flour, using a round-bladed knife to scrape the sides of the bowl. Hold the bowl with one hand, and with the other press the mixture into a ball.
3. Place on a lightly floured board and gently roll with a rolling pin until it is about 5 mm/¼″ thick. Cut carefully into biscuits using a cutter, or cut into even-sized shapes – diamonds, squares or triangles. Place on a greased baking tray, prick with a fork, and put in the middle shelf of the oven for about 10–15 minutes until pale golden. Place carefully on a cooling tray until cold, then store in a tin.
4. Alternatively, the mixture can be pressed into an 18 cm/7″ greased sandwich tin, marked round the edge with your thumb, and pricked all over with a fork. Cook for 1 hour until golden brown. Cut into pieces in the tin and leave to cool.

Chocolate Chip Cookies

75g/3oz butter or margarine (softened)
75g/3oz brown or white sugar
1 egg
175g/6oz self raising flour and a pinch of salt
100g/4oz cooking chocolate or polka dots

Method

Grease a baking tray with melted lard. Light oven Regulo 4, 180°C or 350°F.

1. Weigh butter and sugar into a mixing bowl and beat with a wooden spoon until soft and pale in colour (creaming).

illustrated by Jil Shipley

2. Break the egg into a basin or cup and beat with a fork. Add a teaspoonful of egg to the creamed mixture and beat in hard. Continue until all the egg is beaten in.

3. Weigh the flour and salt into a bowl and sift gradually into the creamed mixture, stirring with the wooden spoon. At the same time add the chocolate, cut into small pieces. Mix it all well together.

4. Place small heaps on the baking tray using a teaspoon and knife. Do not put them too close together as the biscuits spread as they cook.

5. Put in oven and cook for 15–20 minutes until golden in colour. Place on a cooling tray.

Chocolate and Coconut Slices

175g/7oz coconut
175g/7oz sugar
1 egg white (ask a grown-up to separate from the yolk if you don't know how to do this)
100g/4oz glacé cherries – cut into small pieces
50g/2oz chopped walnuts, if liked
200g/8oz plain cooking chocolate – Cakebrand or Scotchoc

Method

Light oven Regulo 4, 180°C or 350°F.

1. Grease a swiss roll tin with a margarine or butter paper.

2. Half fill a large saucepan with hot water. Take it to the table and put a metal plate on top. Break the chocolate into pieces and put on the plate. Using a round-bladed knife, stir gently as it melts. Then, using a cloth to hold the plate, pour the chocolate into the greased tin. Tilt the tin until evenly covered. Leave to set.

3. Mix together in a bowl the coconut, sugar, cherries and egg white, and walnuts if used.

4. Spread this mixture over the chocolate until level.

5. Put the tin into the oven and cook for 20–30 minutes until the top is lightly browned.

6. Cool in the tray, cutting it into pieces when cold.

Chocolate Crumb Squares

200g/8oz block cooking chocolate
1 tablespoon cocoa
50g/2oz sugar
200g/8oz digestive biscuits (broken into small pieces)
100g/4oz margarine (block)
1 tablespoon golden syrup

Method

1. Grease a swiss roll tin with a butter or margarine paper

2. Put margarine, cocoa, syrup and sugar into a saucepan and melt *gently* stirring with a wooden spoon.

3. Put broken biscuits into a bowl and pour the melted mixture over them. Stir until thoroughly mixed.

4. Put mixture into the tin and press down well.

5. Melt the chocolate as shown in the previous recipe and cover the biscuit mixture.

6. When set, cut into squares.

All these biscuits will keep well in an airtight tin.

Doreen Forni

The best Venture of all

by 3rd Langney Brownies

photographs by Norman Redfern

If you've never been on a Pack Holiday, you probably think it's like any other holiday, but it's not! What makes it different?

Well, for a start, everyone helps to run the holiday. We take it in turn to help with the cooking and lay the tables.

Every morning we do jobs in the house, like cleaning the windows. It sound boring, but it's fun when we are all doing it, and by elevenses-time the house is spotless.

An exceedingly good day

by Penny Morris

Do you like Mr Kipling's Cakes? I think most Brownies do, and not long ago a small group of them were lucky enough to visit Mr Kipling's Bakery, at Stoke-on-Trent, as their prize for winning the competition in the 1983 Brownie Annual. Brownies were asked to name a recipe, and the winning entries were: **Brownies' Gold,** sent in by Marinka Huxtable of the 2nd Carisbrooke Brownie Pack on the Isle of Wight; **Brownie Cheese Pot,** by Marianne Jacques of 1st Great Ayton, in Middlesbrough; **Sixer's Scramble,** by Sian Jones of 22nd Cambridge; **Cheesy-capped Brownie,** by Nicolette Lawrie of 1st Bersted, Bognor Regis; **Brownies' Brunch,** by Catharine Morris of 3rd Beswick and Clayton, Manchester; **Powwow Sizzle,** by Claire Robertson of 1st Clarkston in Glasgow; **Elves' Pot of Gold,** by Sarah Sholl of 1st Kingston, near Lewes; and **Cheshire Bubble,** by Jacqueline Young of 4th Thorpe St Andrew, Norwich.

As you can see, the winners were all from different parts of the country so we had quite a task making all the arrangements to get everyone to Stoke at the same time, and for some Brownies it meant getting up *very* early in the morning. Unfortunately, Nicolette and Jacqueline were unable to come, but were sent some presents as a consolation.

photographs by Terry Hope

On the train, Sian and her Mum look at the 1984 Brownie Annual, which had just been published.

When the day finally dawned the Brownies, dressed in their smartest uniforms and accompanied by a Mum or Dad, set off for Stoke-on-Trent and Mr Kipling's Bakery. Sian, Marinka and Sarah travelled via London, so I met them at Euston Station, and we all sat together on the train. As we walked up the platform at Stoke, I was pleased and relieved to see Marianne and Claire with their Mums, and Catharine with her Dad, waiting for us. With them was Mary Hiley-Jones from Mr Kipling, who was going to look after us for the rest of the day.

Mary took us for a short coach ride to an hotel where we had lunch.

The Brownies were impatient to go to the Bakery and too excited to eat much lunch.

After a warm welcome from Mr Patrick Roach, the Bakery Manager, and the other staff, the Brownies put on aprons and caps ready for their tour of the factory.

Sian, Catharine and Sarah were surprised to find the cake batter just the same as home-made cake mix . . .

. . . and the fudge topping tasted delicious!

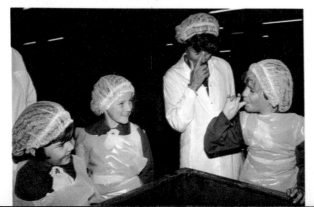

The Brownies were amazed to see so many fruit pies . . .

... and dozens of Black Forest Gateaux!

After a good look round the Bakery, we went back to Mr Roach's office for tea and, of course, Mr Kipling's Cakes!

By this time the Brownies had recovered their appetites and tucked in heartily . . .

. . . leaving little doubt that Mr Kipling's Cakes were scrumptious!

Then it was back to the station for 4 o'clock, laden with presents, after an exceedingly good day.

Our thanks to Mr Roach and all the staff of Manor Bakeries for helping to make our day such a success.

The Snowy Owl

Bird of ill-omen

Does your Brownie Pack have a 'katyogle'? This is the strange name given by Shetland Islanders to the rarest owl to breed in Britain, the beautiful Snowy Owl.

The word 'katyogle' actually means 'cat-faced owl', and the Snowy Owl was given this name because of its large eyes, which are very much like those of a cat – magnificent lemon-yellow eyes which stare steadfastly and almost seem to hypnotise you.

Snowy Owls normally nest in lonely places in Iceland, Scandinavia, North America and northern Siberia, but sometimes they visit the Shetland Islands. At one time the Islanders looked upon them as supernatural birds from a strange land, bringing misfortune and bad luck, and people would shudder to see the 'katyogle', with its five-foot wing span, flying slowly over the countryside.

Even other birds and animals were alarmed. The male Snowy Owl was particularly frightening, being very large, with a thick coat of white feathers extending down to the tips of its claws.

Smaller birds would mob the owl frantically to frighten it away, and any sheep or cow that wandered too near would hurry away when the Snowy Owl hissed threateningly and spread its wings.

In farmyards, hens would cower and look for shelter when the Snowy Owl flew by, and out in the fields cows would low pitifully when they heard the call *tu-hoo-oo-tu-hoot*. Small children would run indoors to tell their parents that the dreaded 'katyogle' had appeared.

The majestic appearance and wise look of the Snowy Owls led islanders to believe that they lived for a very long time, perhaps even a hundred years. They were regarded as serious, thoughtful birds, because they preferred to live in peace and solitude, rather than be near people and the fuss and noise of farmyard life. Snowy Owls pair up for life and once they have chosen a place to nest, they return to the same place year after year.

Before 1967 Snowy Owls had never nested in Britain but in the spring of that year a pair established a breeding territory on Fetlar Island. Soon afterwards, the first recorded nest of a pair of Snowy Owls in Britain was seen, and these birds later produced seven white eggs which successfully hatched into Snowy Owlets.

illustrated by Chris Sheridan **Peter Clark**

MAKE A SNOWY OWL

GIRL GUIDES

This Snowy Owl is easy to make, using items easily available.

You will need:

    one central core from a kitchen roll
    some 'mansize' paper tissues
    Copydex glue
    2 plastic beakers or some white card
    cling film

1. Cut the cardboard core to measure about 10 cm.

2. Press one end together, cut a curved shape, and stick it together.

3. Take four 'mansize' tissues and cut two strips of folded tissue from each.

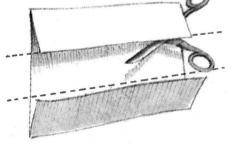

4. Snip 2.5 cm strips, from the fold upwards, along the length of the tissue.

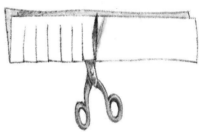

5. Unfold the tissue and blow against the direction of the fold, to make the owl's feathers.

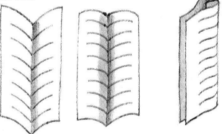

6. Starting at the bottom of the core, stick the tissue all around, continuing until you get to the top.

7. For the eyes, either cut 5 cm from the bottom of two plastic beakers, or cut two circles 5 cm in diameter from a piece of white card, and two strips 14 cm long and 1.5 cm wide. Stick the strips on to the circle edges.

8. Cut two 2.5 cm diameter circles from black card (or colour white card) and place these in each eye. Then cover the entire eye with cling film, sticking it at the back of the eye. Glue the eyes firmly on to the owl.

9. Cut a beak from card, colour it orange, and stick into place.

10. Cut two feet, with long claws, and stick these to the bottom of the owl.

Brownies round the world

If you look at a globe you will see that New Zealand is on the opposite side of the world to the United Kingdom, in the Southern Hemisphere. This means when we have our summer, it is winter in New Zealand, and on December 25th, when you are playing inside, out of the cold, Brownies in New Zealand are probably eating their Christmas dinner out-of-doors, or even on the beach.

Because of its position, New Zealand is one of the first countries to see the sun rise each day. On February 22nd many Guides and Brownies go to a special place, such as the top of a hill, so they can be the first to start the chain of thought that links all members of the World Association on this special day.

Here is a letter from two Brownies who live in Atiamuri:

Box 25
Atiamuri.
8.2.82.

Dear Editor,

Our names are Sarah Robinson and Lynette Wiggins. We are writing to tell you about our pack. We live in a country area where there are lots of farms and two hydro electricity dams.

Lynette's mother is Brown Owl and Sarah's mother is Tawny Owl. There are 20 brownies in our pack and the names of our sixes are Tomtits, Grey Warblers, Bell birds and Pipits which are all native birds of New Zealand. Our drawing is about the

day we had our obstacle course. This was part of our Brownies care activities where we had to do something healthy in the fresh air for half an hour or more we hope you like our picture.

Love from
Lynette Wiggins
and Sarah Robinson.

Tomtit

Grey Warbler

Bellbird

Pipit

52

Lynette and Sarah outside their Brownie Hall.

This is the river and forest around Atiamuri.

Looking to see what lives in the shallow water.

Here we are looking for unusual stones to make stone animals.

Some of the Brownies are making a nature collage.

A game of blind tag.

Here is a picture sent by Claire Solon a Brownie from New Zealand.

Down on the Farm

Have you ever wondered what it was like living and working on a farm around the turn of the century, before the invention of tractors, and combine harvesters, and other modern equipment?

If you would like to find out for yourself you could pay a visit to Acton Scott Farm Museum, situated about four miles south of Church Stretton near Ludlow, in Shropshire. I visited the farm with some Brownies and Guides from the surrounding district.

The farm museum covers 22 acres, and was originally the home farm of a large country estate. During the eighteenth and nineteenth centuries the farm would have provided food for the family living in the Hall. The oldest part of the Hall was built in 1580 and the Acton family still live there. All the animals kept on the farm now are typical of the breeds that lived in this area in the 1900s.

The Guides and Brownies were taken on a tour of the farm. First we walked past the fish-ponds, where the Aylesbury ducks were enjoying a swim. The pond was a very important part of the estate, providing fresh fish to eat in the winter months when meat was scarce.

Beside the pond, two large Tamworth pigs were lying in the mud. They do this to keep cool. It was a very hot and sunny day, and if the pigs didn't keep themselves covered with mud, they might get sunburnt!

Across the farmyard we could hear squeaking and grunting. The Brownies and Guides looked into a pigsty to see the weaners, young Tamworth pigs, about a year old.

Strutting round the farm yard keeping an eye on our activities was Archie, the cockerel.

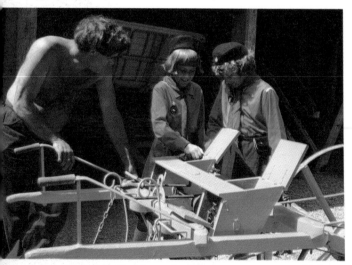

Up near the farm buildings were some old farm machines which were being restored. This turnip drill was originally made by a local firm. Restoring and conserving farm machinery is a very important part of the museum's work.

photographs by Peter Bartlett

Next we went into the cowshed, where there were two Dairy Shorthorn calves. Before the introduction of Friesian cattle (black and white ones), Dairy Shorthorns were the most common.

We walked past the stables but all the horses were out at work. The Guides had a look at a harness that would have been worn by a horse pulling a cart. They were surprised how heavy it was.

Nearby was the wheelwright's shop, where all the wheels for the carts would have been made. Demonstrations of saddlery and wheelwrighting are given regularly at the farm.

Up in the fields we met Bonny, a beautiful Shire horse, and her foal Jewel, who was eleven weeks old. Already she was as tall as the Brownies and when full grown would be about eighteen hands high (one hand=four inches).

At the far end of the field some Shire horses were hard at work ploughing up the soil.

Back in the cowshed it was now time for milking, which is done by hand. The cows produce about six gallons of milk a day, which would have been sufficient for the family plus enough to make butter once a week. Nowadays the milk is used to make cottage cheese and to feed the calves. Cream is bought in for the butter-making demonstrations which take place daily in the dairy.

Visitors to the farm are welcome between the end of March and the end of October, although parties should always book in advance.

Blossom

Can you give each blossom its correct name, and say when each is in flower?

A	Apple	a	late April, early May
B	Almond	b	May
C	Pear	c	mid April
D	Cherry	d	March and April

Pear and Apple photographs
by Michael and Lois Warren
Almond and Cherry photographs
by Jarrold colour publications

Answers are on page 61.

Do You Like

I'm sure you would agree that a British breakfast would not be complete without toast and marmalade, but have you ever wondered where and when marmalade was originally made?

Some people believe marmalade was first made by Mary Queen of Scots' doctor as a cure for seasickness; she always took a few spoonsful before boarding her ship.

Other people say that marmalade first came from Portugal and took its name from *marmelada*, which was a sort of stiff paste originally made from the quince or *marmelo*, and usually served with cheese.

The first marmalade in Britain was made from the bitter oranges brought here in Spanish ships during the sixteenth century. These oranges were called 'portyngales' as they came from Portugal.

The earliest instructions for making orange marmalade appeared in the recipe books of people who worked in the kitchens of large houses. But the first production of orange marmalade on a large scale was by Janet Pierson in Dundee, over 200 years ago.

A large ship with a cargo of Portuguese oranges took shelter in the harbour at Dundee, and Janet's husband, James Keiller, decided to buy a large number of the oranges to sell in his shop. But no one would buy them as they were found to be very bitter, so instead Janet decided to experiment with them. She mixed them with sugar to make an orange jam, and put this on sale in the shop.

It proved to be a great success and the Keillers had to employ many people to help them keep up with the demand for the tasty orange jam, which was soon named marmalade.

As the popularity of marmalade spread throughout Britain other people began making different types to sell. One couple, the Robinsons, made a clear jelly containing finely shredded orange peel, which soon became known as 'Golden Shred'. In Oxford a grocer called Frank Cooper began to sell his own home-made marmalade, made of thickly-cut orange peel, and soon many of the students were eating it, and not only for breakfast.

Although to us marmalade seems out of place at any meal but breakfast, in the eighteenth and nineteenth centuries people would eat it throughout the day. It was often used to make cakes and puddings, and was a popular accompaniment to boiled ham, pork or beef.

Peter Griffiths

It wasn't until the habit of having a really large cooked breakfast died out that marmalade became an essential part of the British breakfast. At one time a typical breakfast might include meat pies, chops, egg puddings, fish, potatoes and bread. But after the turn of the century a more simple, quicker-to-eat breakfast became popular, usually bacon and eggs, followed by toast and marmalade.

Almost every household bought a pot of marmalade every week for the breakfast table.

The earliest marmalade was sold in special stone jars or pots known as galley pots. They sloped outwards from the base up to the rim and had a muslin cover tied on top. Later glass jars were used because they were cleaner and cheaper. The stone marmalade jars are quite rare so if you happen to find one, keep it safe, as it might be worth quite a lot of money to a collector.

You don't have to limit marmalade to breakfast time. Here are some recipes for you to try.

Marmalade Sponge Pudding

100 g (4 oz) soft margarine
100 g (4 oz) caster sugar
100 g (4 oz) self raising flour
1 teaspoon baking powder
2 eggs
25 g (1 oz) coconut
4 level tablespoons marmalade

1. Light the oven at Gas Mark 5 (375°F/190°C).

2. Lightly grease a 1-pint baking dish.

3. Put all the ingredients together in a mixing bowl and beat hard for 2–3 minutes.

4. Put the mixture in the ovenproof dish and bake it in the centre of the oven. While it is cooking, butter a piece of greaseproof paper and after 30 minutes put this on top of the pudding to stop it getting too brown. Bake it for another 15 minutes until it is just firm when lightly pressed.

5. Turn off the oven and take the pudding out. Spread 2–3 extra tablespoons of marmalade on the top and dot with about 1 tablespoon of butter. Return it to the still-warm oven for a few minutes to melt the butter.

    Serve with custard or cream.

Marmalade ?

Marmalade Buns

225 g (8 oz) plain flour
2 level teaspoons baking powder
pinch of salt
75 g (3 oz) butter
75 g (3 oz) caster sugar
1 egg
approx 150 ml ($\frac{1}{4}$ pint) milk
100 g (4 oz) orange marmalade

1. Light the oven at Gas Mark 7 (425°F/220°C).
2. Sift the flour, salt and baking powder into a bowl.
3. Add the butter, and cut it into small pieces with a round bladed knife. Then, using your finger tips, rub it into the flour until the mixture looks crumbly.
4. Stir in the sugar, and then the egg.
5. Add the milk a little at a time until the mixture forms a stiff dough.
6. Stir in the marmalade, then drop spoonfuls of the mixture onto a lightly greased baking tray.
7. Bake in the oven for 15–20 minutes.

Marmalade Apple Cake

50 g (2 oz) margarine or butter
125 g (5 oz) caster sugar
1 egg
140 g (5$\frac{1}{2}$ oz) plain flour
2 level teaspoons baking powder
topping:
50 g (2 oz) demerara sugar
100 g (4 oz) orange marmalade
25 g (1 oz) softened butter
1 tablespoon condensed milk
2 level tablespoons plain flour
2 cooking apples

1. Light the oven at Gas Mark 5 (375°F/190°C).
2. Line a Swiss roll tin (18 cm × 28 cm × 4 cm) with lightly greased greaseproof paper.
3. Cream lightly together the fat and sugar, then add the egg.
4. Sift the flour and baking powder together, then stir into the creamed mixture alternately with the milk.
5. Spread the mixture evenly over the base of the prepared tin.

TOPPING

6. Mix together the sugar, marmalade, butter, flour and milk.
7. Peel, core and thinly slice the apples and cover the cake mixture with overlapping slices.
8. Spread the topping over the apples.
9. Bake for 45–50 minutes.
   Cool slightly then cut into portions and serve with cream.

Marmalade Pudding

3–4 thin slices of brown bread, spread with marmalade
50 g (2 oz) sultanas
1 level tablespoon caster sugar
400 ml ($\frac{3}{4}$ pint) milk
2 eggs

1. Light the oven at Gas Mark 4 (350°F/180°C).
2. Lightly grease an ovenproof dish with butter.
3. Cut the bread into strips and put a layer in the bottom of the dish.
4. Sprinkle some of the sugar and sultanas over them.
5. Repeat with more layers of bread, sultanas and sugar, until they are used up.
6. Put the milk in a saucepan and heat it gently. Remove it from the heat *before* it comes to the boil.
7. Put the eggs in a bowl and whisk them lightly.
8. Pour the milk over the eggs, stirring all the time.
9. Pour the liquid over the bread and leave it to stand for 15 minutes.
10. Bake in the oven for 30 minutes until the pudding is set and lightly browned.

THE SAFFRON CROCUS

I wonder if you have ever planted crocus corms in the autumn, ready for flowering next spring? Did you know that one particular crocus actually flowers in October? This is the purple autumn or saffron crocus, and it has an interesting history.

If you look inside a crocus, you will see thin, strand-like stigmas, which hold the flower's pollen. In the saffron crocus, the stigmas are red, with orange tips called anthers. For centuries, these stigmas have been collected to make saffron, a spice or yellow dye. The stigmas of four thousand crocus flowers are needed to make one ounce (25 g) of saffron!

The saffron crocus was very valuable long ago. People who lived in Ancient Greece thought it a royal flower. It was strewn on the floors of kings' courts or important private houses. Perfume made from saffron was sprayed from small fountains over respected guests.

Elsewhere, too, the crocus was the flower of kings. It was sprinkled in the streets when the Roman emperor, Nero, passed. In ancient Ireland, royal cloaks were dyed with saffron, and saffron-dyed shirts were worn by chieftains in the Hebrides.

In the Middle Ages, saffron was made into a glaze, and printed over tinfoil to look like gold. This was used to make beautiful pictures.

So important was the saffron crocus that many people thought it had magic properties! In Switzerland, long ago, a crocus would be hung round a child's neck to keep away evil spirits.

No one is sure when the saffron crocus came to Britain, but some people believe that King Henry I, who lived in the twelfth century, loved saffron as a spice. He was very annoyed when the court ladies used up his supplies to dye their hair!

Other people say that the crocus was brought to the Essex village of Walden during the fourteenth or fifteenth centuries. A pilgrim, returning from his travels to the East, had hidden the corm of a saffron crocus in his hollowed-out staff. He planted the corm, which flourished and spread so well that the village of Walden eventually became known as Saffron Walden. The people who grew the flowers were called 'crokers', and three crocus flowers appeared on the village coat of arms.

Many medicines were made from saffron. King James I thought saffron could cure measles and other rashes. Saffron was taken to cure heart disease, and was well known for its power to make people happy. A person in high spirits was said to have 'slept on a bag of saffron'. At one time, saffron was even sold in pet shops to cheer up moulting canaries!

Saffron is still used today, to flavour and colour rice dishes. It is very popular in Spain and Eastern countries. If you try to buy it, you will be amazed at the high price. The saffron crocus is rarely grown in England now, so our shops must obtain saffron from abroad.

Yet we can still plant the cousins of the saffron crocus in autumn, and enjoy their flowers in spring. They may not be the flowers of kings, but just the sight of them is cheering!

illustrated by Angela Beard

Jill Weekes

60

Brownies: enter our exciting competition!

Sponsored by Portman Building Society

I'm sure you are all aware of the need to care for our precious wildlife, and perhaps some of you are even working for the Conservation Badge. For several years the Portman Building Society has taken a special interest in the conservation of wildlife, and this year they have generously offered to sponsor our competition.

Together with the Royal Society for the Protection of Birds, the Portman Building Society has been campaigning to help the survival of woodland birds by protecting their habitat, and so for our competition we want you to draw or paint a picture of one of our best-loved birds – the owl.

It can be any kind of owl, Tawny, Snowy, or even an imaginary owl if you like. You can use crayons, paints, coloured pencils, or felt-tip pens, and we want you to draw your owl on a piece of plain paper no larger than 290mm × 210mm. On the back of your picture, clearly print your name, address, age, and Brownie Pack. Also we want you to tell us the three things you like best in this annual. This is very important as it helps us to make the next annual even better!

The first prize is a beautiful pair of binoculars, and the two runners-up will each receive a selection of natural history books.

Send your entries to: The Editor, The Brownie Annual, The Girl Guides Association, 17–19 Buckingham Palace Road, London SW1W 0PT.

The closing date for entries is 31st March 1985. The winners will be notified by post, and the editor's decision is final.

Answers

Who Am I?

Answer: An Earthworm

Front end – pointed

Saddle—

Rear end – flattened

Pantomime Puzzle

1. Jack and the Beanstalk
2. Snow White
3. Aladdin
4. Dick Whittington
5. Cinderella
6. Sleeping Beauty

Blossom Quiz

1 B,d
2 D,c
3 A,b
4 C,a

Rambler game

GIRL GUIDES

There are two ways to play this game. You can follow the instructions in the green footprints and play it as a straightforward board game, or you can work your way round the board trying to complete all the Challenges in the brown footprints.

To play the game – You need a dice, and each player should trace the boot, cut it out of card and colour it in to be her marker. To start you must throw an even number, and the first player to reach home is the winner. You should obey only the instructions in the green footprints, and ignore the Challenges in the brown footprints.

To complete the Challenges – Work your way around the board trying to complete all the Challenges in the brown footprints. As you complete each Challenge colour in the footprint. You can play this on your own, or with a friend, and there is no time limit. There are no winners or losers in this game, but perhaps when you have finished you could find out about taking the Rambler Badge.

Pelican Snap

Using either thick paper or old cereal packets, cut out thirty cards all the same shape and size. Divide them into three piles, and on one set draw a red man, on one set draw a green man, and on the last set draw a flashing green man. Shuffle them together, and play Pelican Snap.

The answers to Challenges 7, 11, 19 and 29 can be found in a natural history book.

1 Learn and understand the Country Code.

2 You visit Guide HQ & St James' Park. Go on 3.

3 Stand outside and list all the sounds you can hear.

7 Find out what an Erithacus rubecula is.

8 Go on 3 to put your litter in the bin.

6 You forget to use the Green Cross Code. Go back 3.

4 Your Six holds a sponsored Litter Pick-up. Go on 3.

15 Go to a museum and write about what you see there.

9 Make a collage using leaves.

5 Draw a large circle and fill in 8 points of the compass.

LITTER BIN

14 You visit a museum and ... your Six about it. Go on 3.

10 You remember to keep to the edges of fields. Go on 3.

11 Find out what Tussilago farfara is.

13 Make a special effort to put all litter in a bin this week.

12 You extinguish a cigarette end thrown from a car. Go on 3.

62